MIXED COMPANY

BOOKS BY IRWIN SHAW

plays

BURY THE DEAD
THE GENTLE PEOPLE
SONS AND SOLDIERS
THE ASSASSIN

short stories

SAILOR OFF THE BREMEN
WELCOME TO THE CITY
ACT OF FAITH

novel

THE YOUNG LIONS

RANDOM HOUSE
new york